YOU'RE THE VOICE
Tom Jones

IMP

International
MUSIC
Publications

© International Music Publications Limited
Griffin House 161 Hammersmith Road London W6 8BS England

Series Editor: Anna Joyce

Editorial, production and recording: Artemis Music Limited
Design & Production: Space DPS Limited
Cover picture supplied by Redferns Music Picture Library

Published 2001

© International Music Publications Limited
Griffin House 161 Hammersmith Road London W6 8BS England

Exclusive Distributors:

International Music Publications Limited

England: Griffin House
                 161 Hammersmith Road
                 London W6 8BS

Germany: Marstallstr. 8
                 D-80539 München

Denmark: Danmusik
                 Vognmagergade 7
                 DK1120 Copenhagen K

Carisch

Italy: Nuova Carisch
                 20098 San Giuliano Milanese
                 Milano

Spain: Nueva Carisch España
                 Magallanes 25
                 28015 Madrid

France: Carisch Musicom
                 25, Rue d'Hauteville
                 75010 Paris

Tom Jones
(born Thomas
Jones Woodward)
7th June 1940

In his native Wales, he is known as 'Jones the Voice', due to his unique vocal power and charismatic persona, and he has peppered the last three decades with memorable hits that showcase his unique talent.

Tom Jones began his long career as vocalist and front-man for local Pontypridd band Tommy Scott and the Senators, and plied his trade in tough working men's clubs and dance halls. It wasn't long before he was discovered by songwriter Gordon Mills, who became his manager and took the young Welshman under his wing, relocating him to London and seeking the fame and recognition such a talent deserved.

Although various record company executives initially dubbed him "too raucous a voice" and "too sexual a performer" and refused to sign him, Tom eventually secured his first recording contract with Decca Records. It was not long before hits like 'It's Not Unusual', 'What's New Pussycat' and 'Help Yourself' had made him a household name and cemented his stature as one of the consummate sex-gods of the '60s.

"Forever-cool Jones, unlike Tony Bennett and Johnny Cash, hasn't aged gracefully. He's aged invisibly, still belting sensual rockers with the hormonal uppercut of a first kiss." (Edna Gundersen, USA Today)

GREEN GREEN GRASS OF HOME

Words and Music by Curly Putman

HELP YOURSELF

Original Words by Guilio Rapetti
Music by Carlo Donida

1. Love is like can-dy on a shelf,
2. We're al-ways told re-peat-ed-ly,

you want to taste then help your-self.
the ve-ry best in life is free.

I'LL NEVER FALL IN LOVE AGAIN

Words and Music by Lonnie Donegan and James Currie

Verse 3:
I gave my heart so easily,
I cast aside my pride.
But when you fell for some-one else, baby,
I broke up all inside.

And it looks like *etc.*

IT'S NOT UNUSUAL

Backing

Words and Music by Gordon Mills and Les Reed

1. It's not un-u-su-al to be loved by an-y-one.
2. It's not un-u-su-al to go out at an-y time.

(Verse 3 see block lyric)

(2° & 3° only)

It's not un-u--su-al to have fun with an-y-one.
But when I see you out and a-bout it's such a crime.

Verse 3:
It's not unusual to be mad with anyone
It's not unusual to be sad with anyone.
But if I ever find that you've changed at any time
It's not unusual to find that I'm in love with you.

Woh, woh, *etc.*

MAMA TOLD ME NOT TO COME

Words and Music by Randy Newman

1. "Want some whis-

(1.) -key in your wa-ter, su-gar in your tea?"
2. Op-en up the win-dow, let some air in-to this room. I
(Verse 3 see block lyric)

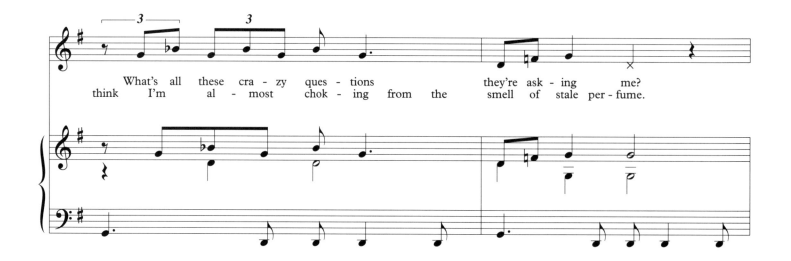

What's all these cra-zy ques-tions they're ask-ing me?
think I'm al-most chok-ing from the smell of stale per-fume.

Verse 3:
The radio's blasting, someone's knocking at the door.
I'm looking at my girlfriend, she just passed out on the floor.
I've seen so many things I ain't never seen before.
Don't know what it is, but I don't wanna see no more.

Mama told me not to come *etc.*

DELILAH

Backing

Words and Music by Les Reed and Barry Mason

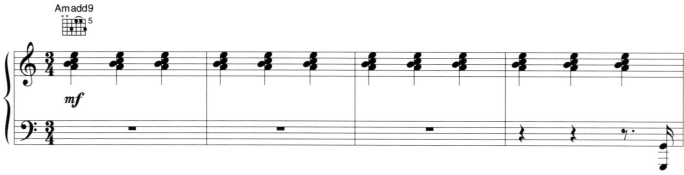

1. I saw the light on the night that I____ passed by her win - dow.
2. At break of day, when that man drove a - way, I was wait - ing.____

I saw the flick - er - ing
I crossed the street to her

WHAT'S NEW PUSSYCAT

Words by Hal David
Music by Burt Bacharach

Verse 3:
Pussycat, Pussycat, you're delicious,
And if my wishes can all come true
I'll soon be kissing your sweet little pussycat lips.
Pussycat, Pussycat, I love you, yes I do:
You and your pussycat lips.
You and your pussycat eyes.
You and your pussycat nose.

SEXBOMB

Words and Music by Mousse T and Errol Rennalls

THUNDERBALL

Words by Don Black
Music by John Barry

1. He al-ways runs while oth-ers walk.
2. He knows the mean - - - ing of suc-cess.

He acts while oth-er men just gives
His needs are more, so he just gives

YOU CAN LEAVE YOUR HAT ON

Words and Music by Randy Newman

8861A PVC/CD

8860A PVG/CD

Casta Diva from Norma - Vissi D'arte from Tosca
Un Bel Di Vedremo from Madam Butterfly - Addio,
Del Passato from La Traviata - J'ai Perdu Mon
Eurydice from Orphee Et Eurydice - Les Tringles
Des Sistres Tintaient from Carmen - Porgi Amor
from Le Nozze Di Figaro - Ave Maria from Otello

Delilah - Green Green Grass Of Home - Help
Yourself - I'll Never Fall In Love Again - It's Not
Unusual - Mama Told Me Not To Come - Sexbomb
Thunderball - What's New Pussycat - You Can
Leave Your Hat On

YOU'RE THE VOICE

The outstanding new vocal series from IMP

CD contains full backings for each song, professionally arranged to recreate the sounds of the original recording

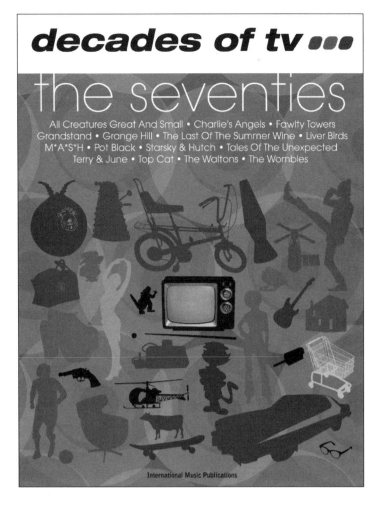

7594A PVG

All Creatures Great And Small • Charlie's Angels • Fawlty Towers • Grandstand Grange Hill • The Last Of The Summer Wine • Liver Birds • M*A*S*H • Pot Black Starsky & Hutch • Tales Of The Unexpected • Terry & June • Top Cat The Waltons • The Wombles

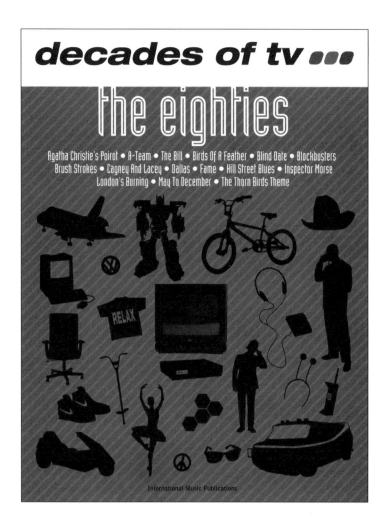

7595A PVG

Agatha Christie's Poirot • A-Team The Bill • Birds Of A Feather • Blind Date Blockbusters • Brush Strokes • Cagney And Lacey • Dallas • Fame • Hill Street Blues • Inspector Morse • London's Burning • May To December The Thorn Birds Theme

coming soon: **the nineties** 7596A PVG

D0TV3